C000152205

# Piano
# Grade 1

## Pieces & Exercises
### for Trinity College London exams

# 2015-2017

Published by
Trinity College London Press
trinitycollege.com

Registered in England
Company no. 09726123

Printed in England by Caligraving Ltd.

# Minuet

Jean-Baptiste Lully
(1632-1687)

Candidates are to play the first repeat only in the exam.

# Melody in C

from *ABC du Piano*

Félix Le Couppey
(1811-1887)

# Melody in C

from *ABC du Piano*

Félix Le Couppey
(1811–1887)

3

# Dance of the Hours

## from *La Gioconda*

Arr. Janet and Alan Bullard

Amilcare Ponchielli
(1834-1886)

# Donkey Trot

Dulcie Holland
(1913–2000)

# Swing's the Thing

(duet part)

Alan Haughton
(born 1950)

# Swing's the Thing

(candidate solo part)

Alan Haughton
(born 1950)

# Ghostly Conversations

Paul Harris
(born 1957)

# The Owl and the Pussy Cat

Mark Tanner
(born 1963)

Composer's original metronome mark is ♩ = 90

# Red Square March

Geri A Rea
(born 1968)

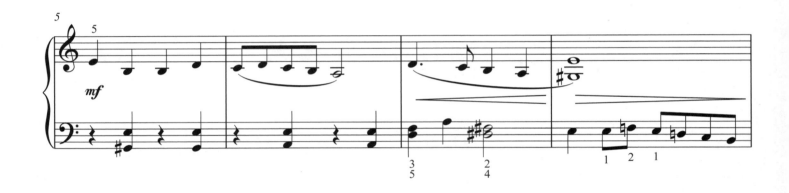

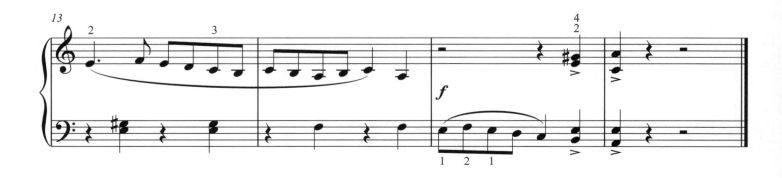

# Railbird Rag

Sam Cleaver
(born 1982)

# Exercises

## 1a. Kit's Waltz – tone, balance and voicing

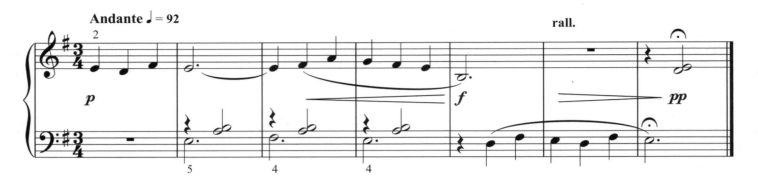

## 1b. Stately Home – tone, balance and voicing

## 2a. On the March – co-ordination

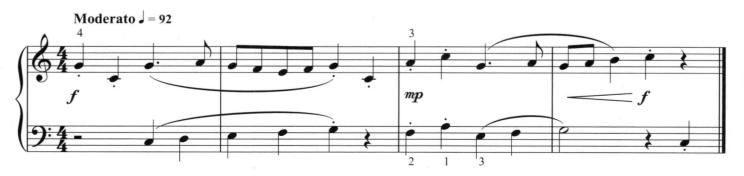

## 2b. The Hedgehog – co-ordination

## 3a. Concertina – finger & wrist strength and flexibility

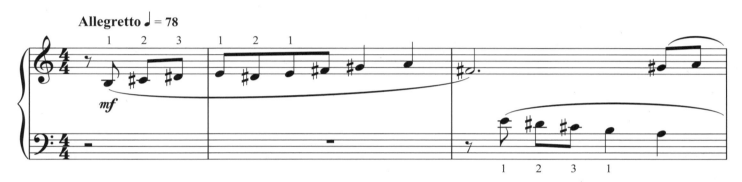

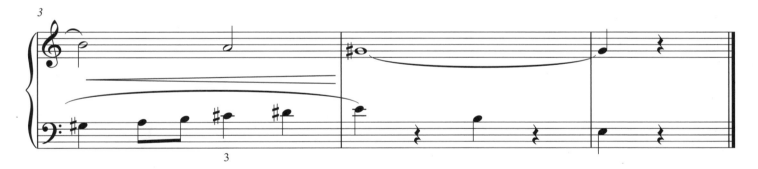

## 3b. The Worm – finger & wrist strength and flexibility